PSYCHIATRY IN THE MODERN WORLD

E. B. STRAUSS

Psychiatry
in the
Modern World

London
MICHAEL JOSEPH

First published by
MICHAEL JOSEPH LTD
26 Bloomsbury Street
London, W.C.1
1958

© *copyright* 1958 *by E. B. Strauss*

Set and printed in Great Britain by Tonbridge Printers Ltd,
Peach Hall Works, Tonbridge, Kent, in Times eleven on
twelve point, on paper made by Henry Bruce at Currie,
Midlothian, and bound by James Burn at Esher, Surrey

'No man can justly censure or condemn another, because indeed no man truly knows another.'

SIR THOMAS BROWNE
(*Religio Medici*)

CONTENTS

PREFACE

THIS is, perhaps, a curious little book from many points of view: it is very short, condensed and easy-and-difficult at one and the same time. It consists of five articles on Psychological Medicine which were commissioned by and published (anonymously) in *The Sunday Times*.

The fact that they were commissioned at all adds yet another element of curiousness to the undertaking. One would not expect a series of articles on orthopædic surgery or dermatology, say, to figure in a Sunday newspaper; yet no one seems to take it amiss or find it odd when a psychiatrist is encouraged to display his wares in full view. Perhaps the chief motive for my compliance was a wish to satisfy, in the least sensational way possible, the legitimate curiosity about disorders of the mind which most intelligent people seem to share nowadays, and at the same time to blunt the appetite of those who would like their psychiatry served up almost in the form of Science Fiction.

This book, then, as its name implies, is by no means a small potted text-book of Psychological Medicine; it is rather an attempt to instruct the interested non-medical reader in how to *think* about psychiatry as a logical category and the place that it could and should occupy in the contemporary scheme of things.

11

In order for that to be made possible, it was necessary for definition to follow definition up to the point where a *pattern* of definitions began to make up a *pattern of thought*.

I supply no nice stories here of people who changed miraculously overnight when they discovered in the course of psychotherapy that *all* their troubles were due to witnessing parental love-making from the cot by the side of the matrimonial bed. No; the contents of this book are just about as unexciting—and as inevitably interesting—as real life. By design, no case-histories were included unless they were necessary to clarify a definition.

If this little book helps to scale the psychiatrist down to life-size, instead of leaving him in the mind of the public (even the literate public) as a mythological construct of non-human proportions, it will have justified its publication between hard boards.

A spate of 'popular' books on psychological medicine and medical psychology pours out from the presses of the U.S.A. every year. Something as impersonal and detached as this book may come somewhat as a surprise in a country where—so I am told—a person talks about '*my* psychiatrist' in the same way as you might say 'my chiropodist.' I have been told, incidentally, of an American with foresight who talked about '*my* mortician' ('undertaker,' as we would say in Britain).

In my opinion, the only person who is rightly entitled to be called '*my* doctor' is a general practitioner; for it is only the *family* doctor who has a close-up view of that important dimension of life.

An American colleague who was visiting England startled me recently by asking the following question, almost on entering the room: 'Are you a Shocker or an

Analyst?' I must unfortunately have confirmed his worst
suspicions of the Englishman as a 'stuffed-shirt' individual, when I drew myself up to my full height and said
rather pompously: 'Sir, I am a specialist in psychological
medicine.' That, as a matter of fact, was the way I
described myself anonymously at the head of the *Sunday Times* articles, which the Editor of that paper so
generously allowed to be published as a book.

1

THE PRACTITIONER AND
HIS FIELD

ALTHOUGH psychiatry is 'news' in a way in which no other branch of medicine has awakened general interest, there is a surprising ignorance outside psychiatric circles as to what a psychiatrist really is and of the field covered by his work. The psychiatrists whom we inevitably encounter nowadays in the novel, on the screen and on the stage are nearly always larger than life: they are either sleek, sinister and yet glamorous or else pseudo-saintly figures—representatives, as it were, of a new, secular priesthood. This state of affairs is probably due to the fact that the minds of most people boggle at all words beginning 'psych' and are unwilling to attempt to arrive at a working definition of them. To test this, I asked about a dozen exceptionally intelligent and well-educated men—including the Editor of a newspaper, a Fellow of the Royal Society, a surgeon and a Q.C.—to define for me: psychology, psychotherapy, psychoanalysis, psychiatry and psychosomatic medicine. All failed to pass the test. It is certainly embarrassing for a physician who specialises in psychological medicine to be introduced at a cocktail party as 'Dr X, the eminent psychologist, you know,' if he does not happen to be a psychologist; and both sides get hot under the collar when the said Dr X is introduced as a psychoanalyst, if he is in fact not one.

It is therefore important, in my opinion, even at the expense of being considered pedantic or tedious, to begin a book of this kind by providing reasonably accurate answers to the Quiz mentioned above.

Psychology is that science which deals with the nature, functions and phenomenology of the mind. It is so vast a subject that it inevitably divides itself into various special branches: educational psychology, social psychology, physiological psychology, experimental psychology, industrial psychology, animal and comparative psychology, clinical psychology, anthropological psychology and a great many other subdivisions. Strictly speaking, no one has a right to be classified as a psychologist unless he has taken a University degree in psychology, or its equivalent. Very few psychologists are, in addition, medically qualified.

Psychological medicine, or psychiatry, in the words of one textbook, is 'that branch of medicine whose special province is the study, prevention and treatment of all types and degrees of mental ill-health, however produced.' A psychiatrist, therefore, is first and foremost a physician, who, like any other specialist, must have enjoyed special training and experience in his chosen discipline in addition to his basic training in medicine and surgery. His general training perhaps lays special emphasis on neurology. Neurology, by the way, according to the Oxford English Dictionary, is the scientific study or knowledge of the anatomy, functions, and diseases of the nerves and nervous system. In other words, a neurologist is more concerned with the structure and functions of the nervous system at all its levels, in health and disease, than with morbid behaviour, thought and emotions.

By psychotherapy is meant the systematic application of psychological principles to the *treatment* of psychogenic ill-health and maladjustment, by which term I mean 'functional' disorders of the mind, i.e. those which are ostensibly psychological in nature and origin. A psychotherapist, therefore, should be a psychiatrist, who owing to special aptitude, interests and training, concerns himself mainly with psychological treatment. However, there are a number of medically unqualified psychotherapists who are for the most part associated with one or other of the special 'schools' of medical psychology, such as psychoanalysis, which itself calls for a special definition.

Psychoanalysis, in its narrower sense, is a special instance of psychotherapy, which derives from the teaching of Freud and the use of the special psychotherapeutic technique evolved by Freud and his orthodox followers. Strictly speaking, no one should call himself a psychoanalyst unless he has had a highly specialised training which lasts four years, and has become an accredited member of The Institute of Psychoanalysis.

As though to complicate terminology still further: the psychotherapists who follow Jung call themselves 'analytical psychologists'—to distinguish themselves, I suppose, from the psychoanalysts; and the disciples of the late Dr Alfred Adler are known as 'individual psychologists.'

The word, 'psychosomatic', will be defined in its appropriate context in a later chapter.

A psychiatrist, then, is a physician specialising in a certain field, and not, as even the average educated person still imagines him to be, a faultlessly dressed man occupying a luxurious suite in the Harley Street area, spending his 'working' time discussing their sex-lives with film-stars and duchesses.

In point of fact, the great majority of psychiatrists work in mental hospitals or in institutions for mental defectives, and are far from being glamorous, elegant or even sinister.

To show you what that means, let me give some statistics which applied to England and Wales at the end of the year 1953: in that year there were 151,320 patients under care in the mental hospitals of England and Wales (direct admissions for the year numbered 72,066). In fact, it has been reliably stated that nearly one in thirty-five of all Britons south of the border will at one time or another be a patient in a mental hospital.

In the same year, there were about 60,000 mental defectives resident in institutions for mental defectives, although the total number of mental defectives in England and Wales is reckoned to be 300,000.

Some 41 per cent of all hospital beds administered by the Ministry of Health are psychiatric beds!

There are no reliable statistics dealing with straight-forward psychoneuroses, psychoneuroses masquerading as bodily ill-health and psychosomatic disorders; but a conservative estimate would be that approximately 40 per cent of patients seen by doctors of all kinds at all times are suffering from the kind of minor ill-health which is largely psychogenic (i.e. mainly psychological in nature and origin). The meaning of the term, psycho-neurosis, will be made clear in Chapter II.

It can be seen, then, that since psychiatrists should know all that there is to be known about the psychoses (the various kinds of insanity), mental deficiency, psycho-

neurosis and psychosomatic medicine, they have very little time left over for dealing with rich old ladies suffering from 'imaginary' disorders, whatever these may be.

However, even that does not cover all the knowledge that a specialist in psychological medicine is expected to possess: he is required to have an expert knowledge of the various social problem-groups in the population: the unemployed and the unemployable, the accident-prone, prostitutes, delinquents (juvenile and adult), psycho-sexual deviants, alcoholics, drug addicts, and many others.

A psychiatrist is not of necessity praeternaturally wise, but, God help him, he must be almost praeternaturally knowledgeable; yet, for some reason or other, he is often expected to be a prophet as well. There are good psychiatrists and bad psychiatrists, in the same way as there are both good and bad doctors of other kinds. For the most part, psychiatrists are over-worked medical men and women employing tools which are possibly some fifty years less advanced than those available for the practitioners of scientific medicine in other branches.

Doctors have always been ambivalently regarded. We do not resort to doctors except under compulsion; for in doing so, we place ourselves blindly in their power. From the point of view of the deep emotions evoked, every doctor is not far removed from a witch-doctor. If that be true of an ordinary medical man, it is doubly true in the case of the psychiatrist.

Although we may resent it if a surgeon tells us that we have cancer of the lungs and must have an operation, we somehow resent it more if we are told by a psychiatrist that we have a depressive illness which requires treatment by electrical methods. A psychiatrist seems to be in a position to wield more power than anyone else. It is he who has to decide that the time has really come for Aunt Clare, who is convinced that she is being persecuted by British Railways and is constantly applying for police protection, to go into a mental hospital—against her will, it may be. It is for the psychiatrist to tell the incensed parents that little James has an Intelligence Quotient of only 83 and could not possibly pass Common Entrance or even his 'Eleven Plus.' How could the psychiatrist be a popular figure? Even so, there is a great difference between awareness of our own prejudices and emotionally over-determined attitudes, and our acting on them as though they were entirely rational.

In the definition of psychiatry (psychological medicine) given above, the last words, 'however produced,' give an indication of the vast field covered by that branch of medicine and lead up to a consideration of a very important, and often neglected, general principle, viz. *the principle of multiple causality*.

There are those who maintain that Aristotelian logic (and the notions of causality deriving from it) is an out-of-date instrument when applied to the medical sciences —and certain other purer sciences. Nevertheless, it will be a very long time before the mental habit of thinking of events in terms of cause and effect is eradicated, anyhow in the field of the applied sciences, such as Medicine. Causal thinking is indeed commendable here, provided that we remember the various types of cause posited by Aristotle—e.g. efficient cause, final cause, formal cause, material cause—and elaborated by later philosophers. Trouble comes about when, in dealing with a medical problem, the enquirer labours under the misapprehension that there must be *one* efficient cause for a given event. Thus, the statement that the *cause* of tuberculosis is the tubercle bacillus, although useful in a very narrow context, is in the last analysis very inaccurate and misleading. In point of fact, there is never one, efficient (or final) cause of a disorder of mind or body, but a chain of causal factors.

In thinking of a given disorder in terms of causation, it is convenient to consider the various factors under four main headings: (*a*) psychic (referring to the life of the mind and the emotions); (*b*) somatic (bodily); (*c*) constitutional and genetic (inherited factors); (*d*) social and environmental (cultural, economic, etc.).

If it were not too controversial, opening up, as it does, a whole field of discourse which is outside the scope of this little book, I should be tempted to add a fifth causal category, to which some psychiatrists, at any rate, would accord significance—'spiritual.'

Causality is discernible at all these four levels in every case; and it is the task of the diagnostician to assess the relative importance of these factors, from the pathogenic point of view, if only in order to arrive at a rational decision as to where to intervene so far as treatment is concerned—which, after all, is what interests the patient most.

What might well be called the main psychiatric *heresies* derive from insistence on one of these causal categories (thought of in terms of efficient cause) to the exclusion of the others.

It is arguable that, among those who think of all psychiatric disorders solely in terms of *psychic* cause and effect, are many psychoanalysts. This bias sometimes leads to the recommendation of psychoanalytical treatment for almost every kind of condition for which a psychiatrist might be consulted. I will indicate in a later chapter what conditions could reasonably be expected to respond to psychological treatment.

Psychiatry also has its fanatical supporters of the view that disorders of the mind are best thought of in terms of disorders of the body—structural or functional. They are the exponents of a psychology and a psychiatry without a psyche. The forms of treatment which they would favour would naturally enough be physical rather than psychological.

Those psychiatrists who are exclusively concerned with a patient's constitution and heredity are not likely to commit positive errors so far as treatment is concerned; for it is impossible to return a patient to his depot and re-issue him with a brand-new set of genes. The only mischief which might be perpetrated by genetical and constitutional fanatics in the field of psychiatry, if there be such, would be to foster an attitude of therapeutic nihilism (therapeutic = appertaining to treatment). For the most part, as will become apparent in a later chapter, such psychiatrists serve a very useful purpose, in so far as they indicate the limited possibilities of treatment, in the presence of certain inherited factors, and also enable us to realise that what is to be regarded as 'normal' in a person of one sort of constitution must be regarded as 'abnormal' in a person of a different stamp—and *vice versa*.

Exponents of the doctrine that psychoneurotic disorders are purely social phenomena, the by-products of an unjust and, dialectically speaking, unnatural social system were to be found in Russia in the early days of the Revolution.

Psychoneurotics would automatically disappear from the population once a Marxist society flourished. Those who nevertheless persisted in exhibiting psychoneurotic symptoms might well be deemed guilty of bourgeois deviationism rather than regarded as sick people in need of psychological help.

If psychiatry, then, is to make a valuable contribution to Medicine in the modern world, accurate diagnosis, which should be based on a sober and balanced assessment of the causal factors mentioned above, must precede consideration of possible methods of treatment.

That is one of the many cogent reasons why a psychiatrist should be a specialist physician of high standing who sees patients only at the request of a medical colleague—preferably, the general practitioner responsible for the patient. In countries where our kind of medical etiquette is not observed and where the standards of professional ethics are not so high as in this country, it is possible for a patient to approach direct any practitioner, medically qualified or lay, and demand psychological treatment—often with tragic and disastrous consequences. Let it be remembered that medical etiquette is not a red-tape system devised for the comfort and prestige of the medical profession, but is the patient's surest protection against possible exploitation or medical irresponsibility.

To return to the principle of multiple causation and see how it works out in real life, for sometimes the various causal factors stand out in high relief: a man was sent for consultation on account of a depressive illness which had followed an attack of influenza which he had had five months previously. The infective illness was one of the somatic or bodily causal factors. He had been living on his own during the past year, since his wife had run off with another man—worry and unhappiness constituting the psychic cause. In consequence, he had lived on tea, bread and marmalade and the occasional boiled egg (he was not domesticated) and was already beginning to show signs of malnutrition and vitamin-depletion—other bodily determinants. It emerged from the history that he was a man who had always been subject to mood-swings, at times being gloomy and morose (this was why his wife had left him) and at other times on top of the world. His inborn temperament represented the constitutional factor. The change in his social circumstances was clear enough. We also learned from the history that his mother had had a depressive attack following the births of her four children. This fact neatly provided the genetic or inheritance factor to complete the 'causal survey,' as it were.

2

DIAGNOSTIC CATEGORIES

In Chapter I, after giving definitions of some important words beginning with the letters 'psych,' I pointed out that the causes of illnesses are multiple and that a useful diagnosis should take causal factors into account, if subsequent treatment is to be rational rather than purely empirical.

The problem of diagnosis is unfortunately still further complicated by another circumstance, the importance of which is not always recognised, which might be called *The Principle of Multiple Diagnosis*. This is a principle which operates only occasionally; but there is, alas, no law of nature preventing a person having two or more morbid conditions simultaneously—even more than one psychic disorder at one and the same time.

When I am bringing out this point in the course of teaching, I put the principle in pithy and aphoristic form and, with some amusement, watch the puzzled brows of my student audience waiting for the matter to be explained. I say to them: 'Do not allow yourselves to be shaved too closely with Occam's Razor.' William of Occam was a monkish philosopher who was born in Ockham in Surrey, in the fourteenth century. One of the important principles of his philosophical system, which came to be known as 'Occam's Razor' reads as follows: *Entia non sunt multiplicanda praeter necessitatem* (essential categories should not be multiplied

unnecessarily). It is a fact that medical students are educated with the principle of 'Occam's Razor' very much in the minds of their teachers, so that a student is made to feel almost guilty if he cannot bring all his patient's symptoms under one diagnostic umbrella.

Nature, however, does not always comply with the rules of scholastic philosophy. Thus, there is no reason against a patient having warty tumours in the bladder (papillomata), Housemaid's Knee (patellar bursitis) and Involutional Depression (the kind of depressive illness which may come on in the fifties or sixties) at one and the same time. Any attempt to account for all the symptoms produced by these discrete conditions does violence to the facts and does the patient less than justice. I have known many a patient with an odd assortment of symptoms of this kind labelled as hysterical when, even from the psychiatric point of view, hysteria was the last thing from which the patient was suffering (hysteria will be defined in a later chapter); and psychological treatment has been recommended.

Thus, the imaginary patient mentioned above should have his bladder condition treated by a urological surgeon, his bursitis attended to by physiotherapy, and his involutional depression, if it persisted, treated by appropriate psychiatric methods (probably Electroplexy— Shock Treatment, as it is often inappropriately called).

Let us now, after a short preamble, consider the major categories under which psychic (mental and emotional) disorders are conveniently classified. In doing so, it is important to realise that we are employing analogical, rather than factual, thinking. It may not have occurred to everybody, for example, that nothing is more abstract than a 'disease,' even though it may have a fancy name; there is, in fact, no such *thing* as a disease. Strictly speaking, the only thing that is presented to our perceptions is a person reacting positively or negatively to a set of noxious stimuli, some of which comes from outside, and some from within. Thus, there is no such *thing* as Pneumonia; but there is a *person* reacting in a typical way to the presence in his lung of pneumococci (or whatever the infection may be). That is one of the reasons, apart from its inhumanity, why I object to students and doctors using the word 'Case' as a synonym for patient.

As long as it is quite clear that all the categories described below are abstractions and employ analogies, it will be safe to proceed.

The descriptive or diagnostic categories employed in psychiatry are as follows: the *Psychoneuroses*, the *Psychoses*, the *Oligophrenias*, the *Psychopathies*, and the *Psychiatric Organic Syndromes* (a syndrome=a collection of symptoms with a common causal origin).

The first analogy that I shall employ, in order to provide a comprehensible definition of the first two categories, involves likening the psyche (the integrated life of the mind and the emotions) to a piece of structure —a motor car engine, for instance.

A psychoneurosis, then, is a functional disorder of the psyche in which the psyche, regarded analogically as a piece of structure, remains intact, and in which insight is unimpaired. [By insight is meant intellectual awareness of the irrational nature of one's symptoms.] Thus, using the motor car engine metaphor: there is a bit of grit in one of the jets of the carburettor; the float is *not* pierced; no major repairs are required; no spare parts are called for. Admittedly, however, with the extremely complicated carburettors of today, a great deal of dismantling may be required if the jet is to be cleared; and it may be absolutely essential to assure the purity and proper filtering of the petrol supply in future.

To make it clearer what is meant by insight: I am, let us suppose, suffering from the kind of psychoneurosis known as *Obsessive-compulsive Neurosis* (to be dealt with further in a later chapter) which causes me to have an obsessive fear of germs and of certain kinds of body-dirt. This compels me to wash my hands at least forty-nine times a day, and to count up to seven every time I soap each finger. I cannot be quite sure that I have in fact performed the purification-rite correctly ('did I really count up to seven, or only to five, when I scrubbed the middle finger of my left hand?') and must consequently start afresh. However, I am intellectually convinced that the whole picture is irrational, even though I can do nothing about it; my *insight* is intact. In other words, I am suffering from a psychoneurosis and not a psychosis.

A *psychosis* is a psychic disorder in which the psyche, regarded analogically as a piece of structure, is temporarily or permanently damaged (there is a *lesion* of the psychic structure) and in which insight is *apt* to be impaired, but by no means always. It is remarkable how often common slang gets to the root of the matter: a person is described as 'cracked,' indicating structural damage to the psychic machinery; or again, he may be said to be 'dotty,' which suggests that the psychic structure is so disintegrated that it reminds one of a *pointilliste* picture—a pattern of dots.

This time, to illustrate *impairment* of insight: I am suffering, let us say, from the form of delusional insanity known as *Paranoia*: my whole life centres round the conviction that I am the rightful Duke of Hampshire, and that my claim to the Duchy would be universally recognised if it were not for the fact that the B.B.C.

(which frequently refers to me obliquely in its broadcasts) and the T.U.C. had entered into a conspiracy to suppress the marriage certificate of my paternal great-grandparents. I have already spent a small fortune in litigation. It is clear that my insight is gravely impaired, for I have no notion that my claims are fantastic.

Oligophrenia is Mental Deficiency in Greek, not that the Greeks had a word for it, so far as I know. There are many forms of mental defect, a description of which is not called for in a book of this kind, but it is convenient to classify the Oligophrenias as primary and secondary. Primary mental defect is due either to genetic or constitutional factors; secondary defect is attributable to birth-injury or injuries or infective illnesses occurring in early infancy. There is a very great difference between mental deficiency and mental illness: a mental defective is unable to reach the stage of mental development appropriate for his chronological age, educational opportunities or pattern of culture. Mental deficiency, then, is primarily defective intelligence, capacity for learning and profiting from experience. 'Mental illness,' on the other hand, of course, is usually a disorder subsequently occurring in a person of normal intelligence, although, in accordance with the 'principle of multiple diagnosis,' mentioned above, there is no law of nature against a person of defective intelligence developing a mental illness in addition.

The division of mental defectives into idiots, imbeciles and morons, in accordance with the defective person's level of mental development, is old-fashioned, slightly objectionable owing to misuse, but still convenient: roughly speaking, an idiot is a person whose mental age never exceeds that of the normal two-year-old; an imbecile reaches the four-year-old level; and there are all grades of dull-and-backward persons, or morons, as they used to be called, with a mental age of four upwards, but falling short of what organised society has agreed to regard as normal for the general run of the population.

It will be clear that many lower-grade mental defectives require special care and training in residential institutions or colonies, in view of their inability to look after themselves or to survive in a complex society. In pre-industrial times, every village, we are told, supported its 'village idiot,' who was a tolerated and popular member of the community.

The kindly and permissive environment and the special educational and training methods provided by modern institutions for mental defectives go a long way towards keeping these people not only happy and healthy, but nowadays also partly self-supporting.

Mental deficiency in itself does not of necessity shorten life; so there can be imbeciles with a mental age of four and a chronological age of sixty-four. The ratio of the mental age to the chronological age, expressed as a percentile, is known as the Intelligence Quotient or I.Q. Thus, a child of fourteen with a mental age of ten would have an I.Q. of $\frac{10}{14} \times 100$, which equals 71 approximately. Such a person would be graded as dull-and-backward.

The mental age is assessed by certain tests—so-called Intelligence Tests—which have, in the opinion of psychologists (not psychiatrists—cf. Chapter I), proved reliable and have been kept up-to-date. This is not the place for a description of any of these tests; but it should be remembered that an I.Q. of 100 is taken as the standard norm, even though a child with an I.Q. of only 100 would find himself in the B or C stream in a modern State school. There are special schools or special classes in ordinary schools for educationally sub-normal children.

With one exception, perhaps, no form of medical or psychological treatment can add to the mental stature of a mental defective, although, as implied above, education and training can work wonders in helping a mental defective to adjust to his environment. The one exception is Cretinism. A Cretin is a person born with a congenital absence of functioning thyroid gland. If the condition is spotted early enough—in the first few months of life—substitution therapy (administering extract of thyroid gland or its synthetic equivalent to the baby and for ever afterwards) can in certain cases lead to normal development of mind and body.

It would be of service, I think, to mention here a defect which is often confused with mental deficiency, and with quite tragic results, namely *Primary Reading Difficulty*. It is a condition which is all too often missed by even experienced neurologists and psychiatrists; nor are there enough educational psychologists who have been specially trained in the remedial teaching of these children.

It frequently happens that a child finds great difficulty in learning to read, write or spell. He is far too scared and ashamed to admit this difficulty even to himself; the consequence is that he sits bored and inattentive at the bottom of the class, unable to take in what is on the printed page or blackboard. As most school-work, after the kindergarten stage, depends on the written word, the child comes to be considered as lazy, naughty or mentally defective. Such children often react to this impossible situation by becoming psychoneurotic or delinquent. A young patient was recently brought to me because he was due to appear before a Children's Court, charged with having deliberately broken windows with stones. He told me that he had done so in order to call attention once and for all to his unhappiness and bewilderment. He had an I.Q. of close on 140; but reading tests showed up a reading age many years behind his chronological age; and it often happens that children of really superior intelligence fall into the group of 'Children Who Cannot Read,' which is the name of a book dealing with the subject.

The condition is usually due to partial word-blindness. When word-blindness is complete, as it sometimes is, the condition is nearly always spotted—for obvious reasons. It is the partially word-blind child who is missed. Word-blindness, which is a congenital brain anomaly, for the most part depends on inability to retain the *image* of a word. Each time a written word is seen, it is as though it were viewed for the first time. The condition often goes with a certain degree of 'right-sided cerebral dominance.' In the case of most people it is the left side of the brain which dominates the picture, with the result that the average person is right-handed, right-footed and right-eyed. With right-sided cerebral dominance, there is a tendency to left-handedness, partial or complete. The term, 'crossed laterality,' is applied to those who are naturally left-handed, *in toto* or in part, and who are brought up to be entirely right-handed in their motor patterns. Fortunately, word-blind children can be taught to read perfectly by special methods which differ in many important respects from ordinary methods; remedial teaching of this kind, as implied above, is usually conducted by *educational psychologists*, familiar with the technique.

The recent Royal Commission which considered the

Mental Treatment Acts, although it made recommendations with regard to the disposal of psychopaths, yet failed to arrive at a definition of *Psychopathy*. I cannot be expected to succeed where the learned Members of the Royal Commission were stumped; but an attempted definition in this book has not got the same weight as one which might have to figure in an Act of Parliament. The definition which follows is bumbling and incomplete, but it does give some idea of what a psychiatrist means when he diagnoses psychopathy.

A *psychopath* is a person who is so constituted that he is unable from the start to elaborate those social sentiments which normally act as an automatic regulator of conduct. It is, if you will, a 'psychic deficiency disorder.' It would be an over-simplification to say that a psychopath is a person who is unable to develop a conscience, unless one examines the nature of the conscience more closely; but that is the long and the short of it.

The adult type of conscience is really nothing more than the faculty of reason applied to the judgement of moral issues; but our conduct is not entirely governed by our informed consciences. There is, in addition, a more primitive and childish type of conscience, with its roots in the less conscious strata of the psychic structure. It is that aspect of the conscience which Freud called the *Super-ego*. The super-ego, however speciously it may disguise itself, is archaic, ruthless, superstitious, pleasure-pain-governed, swayed by Talion law. It is largely formed by distorted, childish impressions of important figures in early childhood (especially the parents). It does not depend on spiritual awareness, but on sanctions typified by immature conceptions of primitive rewards and punishments. Nevertheless, the super-ego is one of our most valuable psychic possessions; for, if we had to rely entirely on reason, every moral decision would be such a slow process that we should be brought to a standstill as active members of society; moreover, the super-ego, which acts instantaneously, has emotional force behind it as a driving power.

To simplify the definition of a psychopath still further, one could say, then, without too great inaccuracy, that a psychopath is a person who never develops an efficient super-ego. If he is normally intelligent, his appreciation of right and wrong is an intellectual experience, which is unsupported by feeling or emotion. I, as a psychopath, let us suppose, *know* that it is wrong to knock an old lady down in the street and steal her handbag, but I do not *feel* that it is wrong.

Many psychiatrists would maintain that psychopathy is not an inborn or constitutional defect (i.e. not genetically determined) but is the result of early-infantile experiences. There is insufficient evidence to prove either hypothesis; but the point is an academic one, for the conjectured experiences took place so early in life that they are irrecoverable by the memory and their results—psychopathic development—irreversible.

Some psychiatrists and social psychologists describe a number of varieties of psychopathic personality—and I, too, have my own pet scheme—but I will be content, for the sake of simplicity, to fall in with the current, popular classification—*Aggressive Psychopaths* and *Inadequate Psychopaths*: an Aggressive Psychopath, in virtue of his forceful personality and the strength of his impulses, combined with the absence of an effective, restraining conscience, is predisposed to anti-social activities, even acts of violence. The Inadequate Psychopath is so poorly endowed with strength of personality and so feebly equipped by nature with the ability to face 'the slings and arrows of outrageous fortune,' or cope even with the slightest checks or discouragement, that he curls up as the mimosa leaf is said to do when the breeze turns from warm to cool. The Inadequate Psychopath, then, drifts ineffectually from job to job, unable to settle or put down roots in society, becoming a burden to his family and later a parasite on the community. If he takes to crime, it is usually petty crime, not requiring much physical courage or ingenuity. If Psychopathy is a challenge to the psychiatrist, which he is not as yet in a position to meet, it is much more a challenge to society as a whole; and society is not altogether justified in passing the buck to the psychiatrist specifically, for he does not know many of the answers.

3

BODY-MIND—MIND-BODY

IN spite of the slightly intimidating title of this chapter, I do not propose to try to solve the problem which has baffled philosophers from the beginning of time, namely the body-mind relationship. I will instead assume that man is a psychosomatic (mind-body) unity and that it is just a matter of convenience whether we prefer to express or interpret events in psychological terms in one case or in bodily terms in another. In any case, all experience, in the last analysis, is psychic. Thus, I have a very painful corn: it is the pain and discomfort—something non-material—which interests me, as the experiencer of the event; the chiropodist, the objective observer, will be concerned with my corn as a collection of horny cells on a patient's toe, exerting pressure on a sensory nerve—and causing pain, or so the patient says. So, it would seem that even a corn is a 'psychosomatic event.'

When a 'mental' disorder is, after diagnostic assessment, found to be *predominantly* organic in origin (see Chapter I—Multiple Causality), we talk of an 'Organic Syndrome' (a syndrome, it will be remembered, meaning a collection of symptoms sharing a common causal origin).

Although the symptoms in these conditions may be mainly mental—e.g. impairment of memory, mental confusion, deterioration of behaviour, and the like—

psychological treatment would not be indicated as the method of choice; for the spoken word (all psychological treatment depends on bilateral verbal communication) could not possibly restore dead brain-cells or arrest the growth of a brain-tumour. Indeed, as obtains throughout medicine in all its branches, there may be no form of treatment that is going to bring about a cure, even if appropriate symptomatic remedies may bring relief and make the patient's life much more tolerable.

Senile decay is, of course, the psychiatric organic syndrome with which the non-medical reader will be most familiar; and Dickens's description in *Great Expectations* of the 'Aged P(arent)' is unsurpassed.

As this book does not in any sense constitute a psychiatric text-book, there is no call for an account of the various psychiatric organic syndromes; but one example, other than that of senile decay, might serve to make my point even more clearly: a young married, male patient was referred because he had recently developed such violent rages on trivial provocation that he was afraid that he might injure, or even murder, his wife in one of them.

Although routine physical examination revealed nothing abnormal, the picture suggested an organic, as opposed to a purely psychological, origin of his main symptom. Moreover, according to his history, he had been severely concussed on no less than three occasions. An Electroencephalogram (a tracing recording the electrical state of the brain) showed an abnormally excitable focus. The character of the wave-form recorded on the tracing showed that the patient's rages were in the nature of what are called in medical terminology 'epileptic equivalents,' which means that his rages took the place of fits. The administration of suitable drugs in this case

37

abolished the rages completely. Psychoanalytical probing into the way in which this man had coped with his aggressive impulses from infancy onwards would clearly have been worse than useless—quite irrelevant, in fact; and a murder might have taken place in the interim.

These Organic Syndromes and the mental complications of other, not so directly related, bodily disorders might well be termed 'body-mind events' rather than 'mind-body' (psychosomatic) events.

The term 'Psychosomatic Medicine,' which is bandied about and misused so much nowadays is one which I, personally, deplore, but which calls for some comment in view of its currency. I dislike the term if only for the reason that, if the principle of multiple causality, which was explained in detail in Chapter I, means anything—and I regard it as one of the most important principles in the whole field of medicine—every morbid condition must *ipso facto* be psychosomatic (psyche has already been defined in this book; soma is the Greek word for body). If bodily factors definitely dominate the causal picture, the morbid condition under consideration should be thought of as an organic syndrome in the sense described above. If psychic factors are quite clearly the main determinants, we are dealing with Psychoneurosis—the psychoneuroses will be dealt with in greater detail later in this chapter.

However, psychiatrists are not always the clearest of thinkers, so certain disorders came to be designated as psychosomatic; and it looks as though the term has come to stay.

Psychosomatic Disorders are disorders which were traditionally thought of in purely bodily terms and in which the psyche is now seen to participate so importantly that the consideration of that factor calls for attention. This notion does not necessarily mean that these disorders will inevitably respond to psychotherapy, although the possibility is not excluded.

Psychosomatic Disorders include gastric and duodenal ulcer, bronchial asthma, ulcerative colitis (a condition characterised by colics and bleeding from the bowel— often fatal in the long run), essential hypertension (persistently high blood-pressure without obvious bodily cause), and a great variety of skin troubles. It is really not quite clearly established as yet whether the psychiatrist (in this instance, presumably, a psychotherapist) is considered to be the right person to tackle these disorders, or whether they remain the concern of the general physician, the dermatologist or other appropriate specialist.

The results of psychosomatic research up to date have, in my opinion, not been too happy, anyhow in so far as the study of the psychic part-determinants are concerned. Research has tended to take two main directions: (1) either type-psychology of a descriptive kind (more about this in a later chapter), so that one could come to talk about a gastric-ulcer type of person, an ulcerative-colitis type, and so on; or (2) the bodily manifestations of the disorder were reduced to conjectured, underlying psychological events, usually expressed in psychoanalytical terminology. The first approach, unless conducted by the most scrupulous, psychologically-trained observer, sometimes develops into a medical parlour game, and is of very little use to the patient anyhow. The second approach, as inferred above, reduces a psychosomatic disorder to a psychoneurosis and thereby makes the use of the term, 'psychosomatic,' otiose.

The mere fact, however, that more and more physicians are prepared to accord a place of importance to the psyche in the genesis of ill-health is encouraging and marks a further retreat from the nineteenth-century bastions of materialistic, mechanistic thinking.

I hope that it will be remembered that in the previous chapter I defined a psychoneurosis as follows: a psychoneurosis is a functional disorder of the psyche in which the psyche, regarded analogically as a piece of structure, remains intact, and in which insight is unimpaired. At this point, it would be desirable to see how the various psychoneuroses differ from each other conceptually; for it is the absence of firm definitions which, in many cases, make thinking in this field so woolly and clear diagnosis so difficult.

It is convenient to classify the psychoneuroses under three main headings: (1) Anxiety Neurosis; (2) the Hysterias—(a) Conversion Hysteria, (b) Anxiety Hysteria; (3) Obsessive-compulsive Neurosis. I realise, of course, that these terms—like all the unfamiliar words that I have been forced to employ—sound a little intimidating and technical; but it is worthwhile overcoming one's natural disinclination to familiarise oneself with new words, if one has a wish to acquire new ideas. If one were making a first attempt to study music, for instance, the musical glossary which one would be required to master would be just as formidable.

Anxiety Neurosis is a psychoneurosis which is characterised by the presence in consciousness of irrational, usually situational, anxiety, often amounting to panic. If, in addition, there are bodily symptoms, those symptoms represent the perpetuation of one or more of the physiological reactions to the emotion of fear. If one is very frightened, one's heart may race or miss a beat; one may sweat or tremble; one may feel sick or even vomit; one's knees feel as though they are going to give way;

40

one may urgently want to pass water or a motion; one may blush or blanch; and there are many other bodily reactions to fear. These, then, would be some of the bodily symptoms associated with Anxiety Neurosis. The word, 'situational,' in this context means simply that the anxiety-attacks tend to occur especially in certain situations, e.g. in tube-trains, in restaurants or eating in public generally, far away from the 'home-base,' prior to an examination, and the like.

We are all naturally somewhat anxious in unfamiliar situations or when circumstances are such that we feel inadequate or insecure; but the anxiety neurotic goes through agonies of anxiety both during an attack and in anticipation of one, over which he can exert very little control. The important sources of the irrational anxiety are often largely unconscious; and it is sometimes possible to arrive at a knowledge of them in the course of psychotherapy. Full awareness of the out-of-date, fearful dispositions which have been relegated to the attics or cellars of the mind may enable a patient to make a much better adjustment to the life of the present, with its various challenges.

The following case-history is reasonably typical of anxiety neurosis: Clive S., a thirty-two-year-old draughts-man from the Midlands was referred for the following symptoms—constant nervous tension and apprehensiveness; panic-states in certain situations, e.g. tube-trains and queueing up for (and meals in) the office canteen; fear of fainting and causing a scene; inferiority-feelings.

His mother, who was still alive, was a 'nervous' type, likewise an older brother. Clive himself had always been anxious, shy, timid and self-conscious. His main source of self-consciousness had been his pigeon-chest.

He had started to suffer from nausea and disagreeable

41

feelings of fullness in the abdomen (unrelated to food) two years previously. These symptoms were largely replaced by panic-attacks in the Underground (fear of fainting) and severe anxiety-symptoms of a general kind.

He responded very well to psychotherapy, with one of my colleagues, and, when last heard of, was substantially symptom-free and proposing to get married.

The Hysterias: the Hysterias are psychoneurotic disturbances which are characterised by two main factors: (a) the 'conversion' into bodily symptoms of emotionally-toned ideas and dispositions which are unacceptable to full consciousness, and (b) the presence (usually discernible) of 'secondary gain.' The bodily symptoms are other than can be accounted for in terms of fear-reactions, which differentiate them from those occurring in anxiety neurosis. By 'secondary gain' is meant the advantages accruing from symptom-formation in relation to the external situation. This point will be made clearer when we come to consider a typical case-history.

In *Conversion Hysteria*, the conversion of psychic experience into bodily symptoms is complete, with the result that the patient's conscious attitude to the social consequences of his illness is one of serene and detached complacency. Thus, one may find a patient suffering from hysterical paralysis who is the 'life and soul' of the ward, completely unbothered by his disability.

In *Anxiety Hysteria*, the process of 'conversion' is incomplete, so that there is residual anxiety experienced as such in consciousness. The anxiety symptoms may be indistinguishable from those occurring in anxiety neurosis, but some of the bodily symptoms will be different from the simple fear-reaction type, and secondary gain will usually be detectable.

The following case-history is sufficiently illustrative

42

to be worth recording: a thirty-six-year-old Sixth Form married schoolmaster was referred for a variety of strange symptoms, chief amongst which were 'blinding' headaches, which usually occurred on Monday mornings, and curious cramps and spasms affecting the right hand, which made it impossible for him to write on the blackboard. The headaches had been diagnosed as migraine, although they were by no means typical of that condition; and he had been carefully investigated by neurologists in an attempt to account for the condition of his hand. His predominant mood was bland and cheerful, although he was faced with the possibility of unemployment owing to his frequent absences from the classroom, especially on Mondays.

In the course of psychotherapy, the following facts were gradually revealed: (a) in spite of a First-Class Honours Degree, the patient secretly (secret even from himself) regarded himself as unsuitable for schoolmastering, as he had no confidence in his ability to impart elementary knowledge to adolescent boys. (b) On Mondays, he was required to teach a Division of the Science Sixth, which included a large number of unusually intelligent, critical and ill-behaved boys.

Secondary Gain is clearly represented in this case of Conversion Hysteria, for such was the diagnosis: his headaches provided an honourable *alibi* from a situation which he 'unconsciously' feared. The cramp in the hand made it impossible for him to write on the blackboard and served as an additional excuse for his absence from the classroom. His illness, taken as a whole, made it possible for him to conceal from himself the fearful aspects of his nature which made the teaching and disciplining of youth an almost impossible challenge.

This man made a very satisfactory recovery and finally

43

decided to accept a well-paid post as an industrial chemist.

Obsessive-compulsive Neurosis—In Obsessive-compulsive Neurosis there is a largely unconscious arrest of, or regression to, *magical* modes of thinking and feeling, however sophisticated and 'enlightened' the patient's conscious attitudes and dispositions may be. It should be obvious enough that all of us are still to a certain extent governed by magic and superstition. We read, for example, that in the course of the recent revolution in Venezuela effigies of the deposed President and of ex-President Peron were hanged in the streets of Caracas, cut down and ceremonially burned; and every year here we burn Guy Fawkes in effigy. There is no difference in principle between practises of this kind and mediæval witchcraft involving the making of wax images of enemies, sticking pins in vital spots and finally melting them in front of a slow fire.

It is the gross discrepancy between conscious and unconscious attitudes, the fusing of the whole with religious beliefs, and the difficulty in uncovering the 'guilt' for which the patient is atoning and propitiating the avenging demons that often make treatment by psychological methods so troublesome, chancy and prolonged.

An account of a typical case of Obsessive-compulsive Neurosis, anyhow of the symptom-picture, was given in Chapter II, to which the interested reader may return.

To revert once more to the principle of multiple causality in a diagnostic context: when it seems clear that the psychic causal factor predominates over the others, in other words, when a psychiatrist can confidently diagnose a psychoneurosis, psychological treatment (psychotherapy) is the method of choice. This conclusion is both rational and logical. The psychiatrist, when undertaking or recommending treatment of this sort, must decide which of the many techniques should be employed; his choice will depend on a number of factors: the patient's intellectual endowment, his educational level, his inborn temperament, the time and funds at his disposal, the suicidal risk (if any), the urgency of his need, and so on.

A very real difficulty is that the number of psychiatrists who have had adequate systematic training in psychotherapy is fantastically small in relation to the needs of the population—this applies both to the National Health Service and to private practitioners.

Another principle which influences my personal choice in this matter is that of the 'limited target': I try to decide in advance whether one should attempt to score an 'Outer' or an 'Inner,' knowing that, on this kind of Range, 'Bulls' are seldom to be signalled. One cannot make a silk purse out of a sow's ear, so the adage tells us; but remember that a sow's ear, properly situated and functional, is a much more valuable object than a silk purse in the wrong place. A patient must be made to realise from the start that a psychotherapist is not a God or a miracle-worker who can 'make him all over' afresh and live his life for him effortlessly and successfully.

Inevitably, therefore, as things are, sedative and (so-called) tranquillising drugs often come to be relied upon as the main form of treatment in psychoneurotic anxiety-states, even when psychotherapy could be calculated to have curative, instead of merely palliative, effects.

Sometimes, it is the external environment rather than internal stresses that give rise to psychoneurotic reaction-patterns. In this case, legitimate attempts to modify the environment may be all that is required to put an end to the trouble. This is especially true of many of the 'behaviour-disorders' of childhood, when a change of school, some well-informed 'parent-guidance,' learning to swim or box even, may alter the balance of psychic forces so effectively as to abolish the child's symptoms.

4

MOOD AND MADNESS

In the last chapter I gave a brief account, with a few illustrations, of the kinds of psychic disorders—the psychoneuroses—which call for treatment by psychological methods. I indicated also that some 'psychosomatic disorders' (so-called) might prove to be the concern of the psychotherapist. I suggested, if only by implication, that other forms of mental illness if properly diagnosed, cannot be calculated to respond to consulting-room methods of psychotherapy. In fact, in the case of psychosis a direct attack on the disorder by these methods of treatment alone is positively contraindicated.

In Chapter II I defined a psychosis as 'a psychic disorder in which the psyche, regarded analogically as a piece of structure, is temporarily or permanently damaged (there is a *lesion* of the psychic structure) and in which insight is apt to be impaired, but by no means always.' The two psychoses about which a well-informed public should have some knowledge, in view of their frequency and social consequences, are (a) those affecting Mood—the Affective Psychoses (Cyclophrenia, frequently known as Manic-depressive Psychosis, and Involutional Depression) and (b) those involving the fragmentation of the psychic structure—the Schizophrenias.

These two groups of psychosis are sometimes termed the '*biogenetic psychoses*' in view of the fact that they

47

seem to be bound up with the very life-process of the patient itself. In other words, constitution and heredity would appear to be the dominating causal factors. As we shall see from the last chapter of this book, constitution and inheritance would also seem to determine temperament (normal) as well as the type of psychosis to which a person may be heir.

We have all experienced grief and unhappiness; and I hope that gaiety and joy have come our way also. If unrelieved, 'irrational' misery and hopelessness characterise the predominating *mood*, we talk of Depression; when the mood is one of apparently causeless, irresponsible gaiety ('euphoria'), fecklessness and restless activity, we talk of Mania.

In Cyclophrenia, as I prefer to call Manic-depressive Psychosis for reasons which will become apparent in Chapter V, there is a predisposition to the occurrence and recurrence of psychotic episodes which are either depressive or manic in character. If one takes a horizontal line as the base-line, making it represent normality of mood and also time-intervals, one can construct any number of diagrams and be sure of finding something corresponding to each one of them in real life. Thus, the following diagram would represent the Simon-pure form of Cyclophrenia—*folie circulaire*, as the French call it.

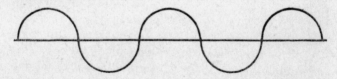

In this condition, fortunately rather rare, the patient never sails on an even keel, so to speak: he is either pathologically exalted or psychotically depressed. If the distance between two turning-points represents a time-interval of four months, let us say, the picture would be one of four months' mania followed by four months' depression followed by four months' mania, and so on. Such a patient, if his symptoms were socially disabling, would probably have to spend most of his life in the protective environment of a mental hospital.

The next diagram represents a much more common picture, namely Recurrent Endogenous Depressive Psychosis. The word 'endogenous' means determined from within, rather than from without (exogenous).

The horizontal line, as a time-scale, between abscissa, can represent anything from days to months (or even years) to accord with the particular case.

This diagram clearly represents Recurrent Endogenous Mania; and no more need be said about it.

The next two diagrams, given in miniature, represent Chronic Endogenous Depressive Psychosis and Chronic Endogenous Mania respectively.

Depression, in the clinical sense, implies much more than simple unhappiness or despair. The following is a list of the major symptoms met with in Depressive Psychosis. The presence of a number of these symptoms, even when depression (with a small 'd') does not dominate the picture, makes the diagnosis of Depressive Psychosis extremely likely. They are: depression; difficulty in concentration; loss of interest in everything; finding everything, especially routine activities, an effort; insomnia, with early waking; impaired appetite; loss of weight; flatulent dyspepsia; diminution of sexual appetite and performance; self-reproach and self-depreciation. with irrational guilt-feelings; tearfulness; suicidal impulses; retardation; fatiguability; irritability.

The picture can, of course, show wide variations, but is, nevertheless, sufficiently clear to make it seem curious that the diagnosis is so frequently missed. It is, for example, an almost every-day experience for a psychiatrist to have referred to him a patient with Depressive Psychosis, labelled 'Anxiety State' or some other form of psychoneurosis.

Manic States are much rarer and need not detain us much. Here are a few of their characteristics: irrational gaiety; restless activity; general disinhibition (lack of control of impulses normally well under control); extravagance in all directions—money, dress, gambling, etc.; impaired appetite (a patient is usually too 'busy' to sit down to eat a proper meal); insomnia; hypereroticism; an interfering type of 'bossyness' and impatience; irritability and angry rejection of criticism. The mind races at 60 m.p.h. in a built-up area, so to speak, and shoots all the traffic-lights.

To give an unusually respectable illustration of the symptom which I have labelled 'hyper-eroticism': a friend of mine who was chronically hypomanic (by hypomania is meant a 'dilute' manic state, in which

50

the majority of the symptoms do not as a rule call for psychiatric interference) became engaged to two different girls on one and the same day. He came to consult me— not professionally—as to which of the two he ought to marry, and did not regard it as at all odd.

The other important Affective Psychosis is *Involutional Depression*. The involutional period of life occurs round about the fifties and sixties—rather earlier in the case of women. It is a period in one's life-cycle when, in the words of one writer: 'the body-chemistry changes, when the glands of internal secretion begin to fail, when the bodily processes decline and the organism fails. The person loses his elasticity and vigour, he can no longer adapt himself easily to these new events and situations in his life which entail strain and stress. Life loses a little of its savour and romance so much so that someone described the climacteric as the smouldering fire of the endocrines in which, from time to time, certain embers flare up, emit sparks and subside into cold ashes.'

The symptom-picture in Involutional Depression or Involutional Melancholia, as it is often called, closely resembles that of Edogenous Depressive Psychosis. The main differences are a greater degree of anxiety, often amounting to agitation, absence of marked retardation, and the occurrence in some cases of delusions of ill-health, unworthiness, poverty, impending ruin and damnation.

Characteristically, Involutional Depression crops up in people who have not previously suffered from depressive episodes. Attacks of Endogenous Depressive Psychosis usually resolve themselves after a time (a duration of from three to six months is common), regardless of treatment or absence of treatment. Untreated Involutional Depression, however, tends to go on for years or may never resolve. It can be said of the condition before the days of Electroplexy (electrical shock treatment) that about a third of the patients recovered after an illness of some years' duration; about a third improved after an equally long illness; and about a third went down to the grave in a crescendo of misery and despair.

The treatment of depressive states (and some acute manias) by means of Electroplexy marks one of the major therapeutic advances of modern times in the field of psychiatry.

The technique was elaborated originally in the Psychiatric Clinic of the University of Rome by Professor Cerletti and his collaborators shortly before World War II, and began to be practised in this country in the early days of the war—late 1939, early 1940. It is nowadays so much the recognised, specific form of treatment for well-established depressive syndromes and involutional melancholia that it is difficult to think back to the days before it was available.

It is a form of treatment which lends itself in properly selected cases to out-patient use, so much so that the number of depressed patients who are required to seek admission into a mental hospital is enormously reduced. Nowadays, indeed, it is quite difficult to find a typical depressive patient in a mental hospital to demonstrate to a medical-student audience.

Between eighty and ninety per cent of properly selected involutional depressives respond to the treatment without relapsing. Some psychiatrists would give a much higher relapse-figure. In my experience, the average number of treatments required is ten, given at the rate of two a week. Psychiatrists differ amongst themselves on this point; but I believe that more harm is done by too few treatments than a few too many. On the other hand, excessive treatment of this kind is to be avoided, if possible.

The treatment is usually given after the injection into a vein of a light anæsthetic and a drug which relaxes all muscles.

In Cyclophrenia, it must be remembered, the treatment can only tackle the attack of the moment, and does not seem to affect a patient's cycle—i.e. the likelihood of future attacks. It is much fairer, therefore, when another attack occurs, after the previous attack has been successfully resolved by means of Electroplexy, to talk of 'another attack' and not to employ the term, 'relapse.'

It was certainly a gratifying experience for psychiatrists to find themselves now able to 'cure' Involutional Depressives in five weeks, say, instead of being the helpless spectators for years on end of unrelievable misery occurring in blameless and worthy middle-aged men and women.

The Schizophrenias: it will be noted straight away, I hope, that the title of this heading is the Schizophrenias and not Schizophrenia, for it is certain that there are a number of disorders which lead to a fragmentation of the personality-structure which are of different causal origins, and have a different 'natural history' and prognosis. Let it be said at once that the word schizophrenia, and its adjective, schizophrenic, are, like most psychiatric terms, generally misused. The word does not mean, and never has meant, 'split personality,' in the Jekyll-and-Hyde or Three-Faces-of-Eve sense—the correct term for that kind of phenomenon, if it exists, being *'multiple personality'*—but something quite different.

Schizophrenia is the commonest and most terrible form of insanity which afflicts humanity; and it would

D*   53

seem to be on the increase. There are in the mental hospitals of England and Wales alone some 140,000 schizophrenic patients; and it is likely that for every one in hospital there are two or three outside.

The causes of this scourge are still obscure, with the result that all forms of treatment are 'hit-or-miss,' empirical procedures. It was reported in *The Times* of February 11th that a British-educated scientist had been given a grant of £210,000 by the American Cancer Society to support him in a life-time of research to seek a cure for cancer. The average expenditure on research into the causes of schizophrenia in this country over the last five years has been £7,500 per annum, according to Merrick Winn, writing in the *Daily Express*!

Over twenty per cent of new admissions into mental hospitals and well over fifty per cent of those remaining in hospital are suffering from one or other of the schizophrenic psychoses. Both the chronicity of these disorders and the fact that they do not shorten life to any extent emerge from these figures.

Some two-thirds of the cases start between the ages of fifteen and thirty—hence the term, *dementia praecox* (early dementia), which was the designation of the disorder before schizophrenia came to be preferred, and which is still the official term in the U.S.A. In addition to the tendency for the condition to declare itself in adolescence, the term, 'dementia praecox,' indicates that the unrecovered patient finally becomes demented (mentally disintegrated).

As will become apparent in the final chapter, a certain type of person, if he has an inborn predisposition to psychosis, is more likely to develop Schizophrenia than the type of person who is predisposed to Cyclophrenia. The genetic factor, therefore, is strong; but we do not know clearly as yet what is inherited or how it works. It seems likely at the moment that the defect is in the chemistry of the body, including the secretions of the ductless glands, and in the physiological forces which maintain proper balance. It is possible that British-born biochemists and psychiatrists who have been driven abroad owing to lack of encouragement and support for psychiatric research in this country will discover the answers and that more rational forms of treatment and prevention will be forthcoming in the light of this new knowledge.

This is not a suitable place for an account of the many symptoms which characterise the Schizophrenic Psychoses. It must suffice to say that, when a schizophrenic syndrome is well established, the patient presents a picture which the average layman associates with the idea of *madness*. For instance, it is in the schizophrenic psychoses that symptoms such as hallucinosis and delusion-formation, with defective insight, crop up most consistently.

Here again, I feel that there is a need to define hallucination and delusion, seeing that most people employ these terms quite incorrectly—in fact, as though they meant the same thing. A *delusion* is a disorder of judgement. It is the holding with unshakeable conviction of an idea or set of ideas which another member of the deluded person's own age-group and culture-pattern would immediately recognise as false. Thus, if I, as a member of the Wonga-Tonga Tribe of Central Australia set out a saucer of milk under a wattle tree in the belief that the spirit of my grandmother, in the form of a serpent, will come down from the tree and lap up the milk, I am *not* deluded; for the fellow-tribesman of my own age-group will share my belief. On the other hand, when I claimed to be the rightful Duke of Hampshire in Chapter II, I was clearly deluded, because there would be no one else in my environment (I am still outside a mental hospital, let us suppose) who could fail to spot the falsity of my judgement.

An *hallucination* is a disorder of perception: it is a perceptual experience occurring in the absence of the appropriate sensory stimulus. *'Is it a dagger that I see before me, the handle toward my hand?'* There was, of course, no dagger; but Macbeth perceived one—visual hallucination. Hallucinosis (the state of being hallucinated) can affect any of the senses; but auditory hallucinations are most common in schizophrenic states.

One very short case-history might serve as an illustration of one of the forms of the disorder: a fourteen-year-old boy, William S., from Suffolk, was referred on account of the following symptoms: he seemed to exist in a world of fantasy and day-dreaming and appeared to have lost interest in external reality. He concerned himself with remote, abstract ideas, such as comparative religion, the Far East, atomic warfare and the like. He heard voices which told him that he had a special mission to prevent 'two hundred thousand thugs' in Soviet Russia from making use of atomic power to start a third world-war. His general mood was one of listlessness and apathy. For example, he had no consideration for his parents' anxiety if he were to run away and disappear for a while, as he had done on two previous occasions, in response to the behest of his 'voices.' I explained to William that, as the result of rapid and uneven pubertal development, little cracks had begun to appear in his personality-structure, which required 'cementing up,' and that the best way of effecting this was by his accepting the type of physical treatment that I would recommend.

William exhibited the type of temperament and physique which are frequently associated with schizophrenic illness; and, as inferred above, I will wind up this book with a brief account of 'Type Psychology' and 'Type Psychiatry.'

PHYSIQUE
AND TEMPERAMENT

IT would seem that there has always been a tendency in human thought to reduce the particular to the general, as well as the general to the particular. Scientists, in view of their approach to phenomena, are naturally more interested in the former method, namely the fitting into general categories of individual units; this is, in fact, an important part of the scientific method. Such a process is of its very nature bound to start from empirical observation; if such observation shows signs of proving of value, confirmatory evidence builds up snowballwise, until a scientifically based hypothesis finally emerges. Does this process apply to medicine, psychology and psychological medicine; in other words, can we humans regard ourselves as 'types' as well as individuals? Attempts to establish systems of human 'typology' have been made since the days of the ancient Greeks right up to modern times, some of which have even sought to establish a correlation between physique and temperament, a 'psychosomatic' concept, in the best sense.

Modern typological systems include that of the great American psychologist, the late William James (brother of Henry James, the novelist), who divided men and women into two main temperamental categories—the 'tough' and the 'tender.' Another modern classification which achieved great popularity is that of C. G. Jung, whose two main temperamental types are termed 'extravert' and 'introvert.' His sixteen sub-types of temperament were built up on this simple, dual classification. The inescapable fact which emerges from all systems of human typology is that a certain kind of body-structure and temperamental patterning are determined for each of us from the moment of conception. Men are *differently* constituted; Biology knows nothing about the 'equality of man,' which is a theological, not a biological, doctrine, and which has been erected by a strange quirk into a political slogan.

In my opinion, the most interesting and valuable system of type-psychology and type-psychiatry is that of Ernst Kretschmer, Professor of Neurology and Psychiatry at Tübingen University. Kretschmer's work is worth detailed consideration in this book if only for the reason that it throws a great beam of light on the two major psychoses which were described in my last chapter —Cyclophrenia and Schizophrenia. His theories depend entirely on *observations*, of a kind which have been amply confirmed in all parts of the world over the past forty-five years, and make no use of unprovable or unlikely theoretical assumptions on human phylogeny (the evolution of the species) or ontogeny (the development of the individual), as do certain other systems purporting to correlate physique, temperament and psychosis. Moreover, in establishing body-type, Kretschmer's measurements are restricted to the skeleton, which does not alter after late adolescence, and do not, as certain other typologists' do, include the soft tissues, which are constantly changing, both in health and disease.

To quote from the chapter on The Temperaments in Kretschmer's *Text-book of Medical Psychology*, it is an interesting fact that 'the principal groups of the constitutional endogenous psychoses can serve as guides through the entanglements of the constitutional psychology of the individual.'

It would seem that certain biogenetic correlations exist in nature, which enable one to discern and describe certain typical patterns of physique which are apt to be associated with corresponding types of normal temperament, certain psychopathic variants of that temperament and a predisposition (in the presence of certain genes) to related types of psychosis.

The three main types of physique which can be readily distinguished by inspection and measurement (and accurately determined by certain mathematical indices) are, in Kretschmer's terminology, pycnosomatic (from a Greek word meaning 'thick-set,' and soma, body), leptosomatic (leptos in Greek means slender), and athletosomatic (athletes, in Greek, of course, meaning an athlete).

Pycnosomatics are thick-set, short and (in middle age) 'tubby' people. Leptosomatics are slender and more 'cylindrically' built. The extreme type of athletosomatic is perhaps best represented by the average person's idea of the heavy-weight boxer. Any artist who abstracts the human form in simple geometrical terms might well portray the pycnosomatic as a square person, the leptosomatic as a rectangular individual and the athletosomatic as trapezoidal.

Persons whose physical configuration differs grossly from these accepted norms—especially, perhaps, with reference to the soft tissues of the body—are known as dysplastic. The chief dysplasias (anomalous forms) are the result of either complete or partial developmental arrest, such as the various types of infantilism and

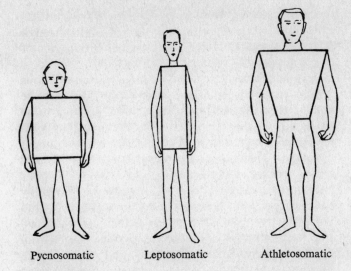

Pycnosomatic   Leptosomatic   Athletosomatic

dwarfing, or of disorders of the glands of internal secretion. A study of these anomalies of body-form yield valuable information on the many kinds of relationship between body and mind, but they need not concern us further in this book.

The type of temperament (normal) which *tends* to go with the pycnosomatic build is known as *cyclothyme*. With reference to mood, the following descriptive adjectives might apply to one or other of the three main types of cyclothymic temperament: cheerfully elated; irascible; 'sunny'; quietly humorous; quietly tenderhearted; heavily dejected; alternations of mood between cheerful and sad. From the point of view of psychic tempo and tension, cyclothymes have some of the following characteristics: smart, pushing and bustling; abounding in ideas; lively and excitable; fluid energy; ponderously inhibited. The social attitudes of the various

61

types of cyclothyme may be summed up as follows: extraverted (turned outwards); realistic; sociable; open; matter-of-fact; materialistic. Some ninety-four per cent of pycnosomatics exhibit a predominantly cyclothymic temperament.

About seventy per cent of leptosomatics exhibit the *schizothymic* temperament. Applying the same scheme to the three main types of schizothymes as we did above in the case of cyclothymes, the picture would work out as follows. Mood and sensibility: 'sensitive plant'; delicacy of feelings; irritable, excited, nervous; cool; severe; harsh; cold; obtuse, indolent; alternations of mood—ecstatic, pathetic, annoyed, nervous, bad-tempered. Psychic tempo and tension: distraught; moody by fits and starts; consistently energetic; tenacious; pedantic; fanatical; inhibited. Social attitudes: idealistic; reformer; revolutionary; systematically organising; stubborn, wrong-headed; discontented, reticent, suspicious; 'lone-wolf,' unsociable; misanthropic; brutal, anti-social. The movements and gestures of schizothymes tend to be: rash, hasty, fidgety; shy; reserved, aristocratically stiff; angular. This contrasts with the motor patterns of cyclothymes which are for the most part mobile, rounded, and 'comfortable.'

In addition to the positive correlation between pycnosomatic build and cyclothymic temperament, there is a striking correlation between that type of body-build and Cyclophrenia (Manic-depressive Psychosis). Thus, in a survey of 1,361 cyclophrenic patients 64.5% were of pycnosomatic build; 19.2% leptosomatic; 6.7% athletosomatic; 1.1% dysplastic; 8.4% uncharacteristic.

There is also a striking correlation between leptosomatic physique and schizophrenia. In a series of 5,233 schizophrenic patients, 50.3% were leptosomatic; 13.7%

pycnosomatic; 16.9% athletosomatic; 2.5% dysplastic; 8.6% uncharacteristic.

The affinities of a certain type of temperament and disease which go with athletosomatic physique, although of great interest, are, on the whole, less impressive and less well substantiated. It may suffice to say that the less complicated type of athletosomatic is often phlegmatic; but that, athletosomatics taken as a whole, are somewhat passive, and this passivity is reflected in their type of humour and social contacts, exhibiting, as they do, difficulty in getting off the mark quickly. The feature common to all these qualities is tenacity. In fact, the type of temperament for which athletosomatics show an affinity has been termed 'collodethymic,' meaning viscous or tacky.

It will be noted that I mentioned three main types of cyclothymes and three of schizothymes. This accounts for what might at first sight appear to be discrepancies in the adjectives used to describe them. It is convenient to differentiate cyclothymes into hypomanics, who are consistently cheerful and sprightly; syntonics who are practical, realistic, comfortable and humorous; and the 'sluggish' type of cyclothymes who are soft, kindly and rather inhibited.

Some schizothymes belong to the hyperæsthetic group, who are delicate-minded, introverted, sensitive, 'nervous' and idealistic. 'Medium' schizothymes tend to be cool, energetic, systematic, consistent, calm and 'aristocratic.' Anæsthetic schizothymes (hyperæsthetic means 'with excessive feelings'; anæsthetic literally means 'without feelings') are chilly, 'odd fish,' queer, indolent and unfeeling.

Collodethymes tend to be either explosive or phlegmatic.

63

To round off the picture it could be pointed out that there are also three types of psychopathy corresponding with the three chief biogenetic groups: cycloid, schizoid and epileptoid. However, a detailed description would be out of place in a short book of this kind. Nevertheless, to demonstrate how neatly it all works out, I append the following table; but the third group is less well differentiated than the first two and can be disregarded for our present purposes.

Physique	Temperament	Psychopathy	Psychosis
Pycnosomatic	Cyclothyme	Cycloid	Cyclophrenia
Leptosomatic	Schizothyme	Schizoid	Schizophrenic
Athletosomatic	Collodethyme	Epileptoid	Epileptic Psychoses

Medicine in all its branches belongs in the last analysis to the biological sciences, i.e. those sciences which are concerned with living things. If all the observations on physique, temperament and psychosis and the genetic links connecting them are sound, we can begin to see a biologically rooted scheme of things in the human constitution, and a pattern begins to emerge out of what previously appeared to be muddle and chaos. Moreover, it is a scheme which fits in with the principle of multiple causality and is therefore much more likely to be correct than more speculative hypotheses which take stock of only one group of possible causal factors and exclude the others.

All this is of much more than purely scientific interest and importance, for it has great practical application in the field of psychological medicine and psychology in all its branches. For example, in the modern world, especially perhaps in America, extraverted attitudes are over-valued, and introversion is apt to be regarded as 'abnormal' and anti-social. Everyone, it would seem, aspires to be husky, hail-fellow-well-met, slap-you-on-the-back-have-a-drink-old-man, the life-and-soul-of-the-party, etc.: and the quiet, somewhat reserved thinker is made to feel odd-man-out. Nevertheless, it is impossible by psychotherapy, or for that matter by any other means, to convert a schizothyme temperament into a cyclothyme variety; but skilful educational methods and re-educational psychotherapy can train such schizothymic individuals as require it so that an essentially social character can develop in the soil of the schizothyme temperament. It is useful and expedient to conduct an analytical investigation in the course of psychotherapy 'down to the level' of a patient's temperamental make-up; by which time the patient will have acquired sufficient insight into his hidden aims and motives to adjust his individual self to the needs of reality. Thus, it can be seen that a knowledge of type-psychology and type-psychiatry has very great relevance for a psychotherapist who is not completely committed to any closed system.

Again, a diagnosis of physical type and a careful enquiry into a patient's temperamental pattern prior to his psychotic breakdown, have a very great bearing on prognosis and may even influence treatment.

Kretschmer quotes from Julius Caesar on the fly-leaf of Part I of his first book, *Physique and Character*:

Caesar: Let me have men about me that are fat;
　　　　Sleek-headed men, and such as sleep o' nights:
　　　　Yond Cassius has a lean and hungry look;
　　　　He thinks too much; such men are dangerous.

65

Antony: Fear him not, Caesar; he is not dangerous;
        He is a noble Roman, and well given.

Caesar: Would he were fatter! . . .

Shakespeare, it would seem, had an intuitive know-ledge of the possible affinities between type of body-build and type of temperament. Novelists, poets, film directors and creative artists in general should have a knowledge of this recent chapter in psychiatry and applied psychology, if their work is to be convincing in the modern world.

All the great men of letters had the same kind of intuitive appreciation of these things as Shakespeare had. Certainly, Cervantes did not put a foot down wrong when he made the dreamy, idealistic, fantastic Don Quixote as thin as a rake, and Sancho Panza short, tubby and cyclothymic. The Fat Boy in *Pickwick Papers*, with his attacks of compulsive sleep, is a beautifully observed and described example of a certain type of dysplastic individual exhibiting a type of disorder which corresponds very well with his type of dysplasia. Mr Pickwick, himself, is perfectly true to type—pycno-somatic and cyclothymic.

What I have tried to do in this book is primarily to create a climate of thought in which the literate public can appreciate the part played by psychiatry and psychiatrists in the modern world, without prejudice or *parti pris*. I have also tried to correct many of the current misconceptions and wrong notions which bedevil the whole picture in the eyes of the public. I have lifted a corner of the gauze curtain which ordinarily makes everything on the other side of it seem so mysterious. I have done this to the best of my ability without sensationalism or recourse to therapeutic-success-stories, which, in condensed form, make things seem much simpler than they really are. In fact, references to treatment have been few and far between, as well as guarded.

From now onwards, anyone who thinks that psychiatry is coterminous with psychotherapy in any of its forms, important though the latter undoubtedly is as one of many forms of treatment in psychiatry, should feel slightly ashamed. Likewise, people who glibly, but ignorantly, makes use of terms such as 'inferiority complex' or the 'Oedipus complex' with the implication that they have satisfactorily *explained* a highly complex series of psychic or psychosomatic events, should also blush, especially if they believe that a few visits to a psychiatrist's consulting room will necessarily put things right.

If I had been asked to suggest alternative titles to *Psychiatry in the Modern World*, I might have favoured 'The Intelligent Man's and Woman's Guide to Psychological Medicine,' or (remembering my first reading book, *Reading Without Tears*) 'Psychiatry Without (Too Many) Tears.' As I said before, this book is not in any sense in the nature of a potted text-book; in fact, I have barely touched on the fringe of the fringe of the vast subject with which I have been dealing. For example, there is in process of publication by a firm of German publishers a work dealing solely with the psychoneuroses and their treatment, which, in spite of coming out in twenty-five large fascicles, has very little to say about psychoanalysis, which in itself is a huge subject with an enormous literature.

We are told that a little learning is a dangerous thing; but knowledge of the extent of our ignorance may be the beginning of wisdom.

INDEX

69